IMAGINE THAT

Licensed exclusively to Imagine That Publishing Ltd
Tide Mill Way, Woodbridge, Suffolk, IP12 1AP, UK
www.imaginethat.com
Text copyright © 2020 Imagine That Group Ltd
Illustration copyright © 2020 Zhanna Ovocheva/Shutterstock.com
All rights reserved
0 2 4 6 8 9 7 5 3 1
Manufactured in China

Written by Joshua George
Illustrated by Zhanna Ovocheva

ISBN 978-1-80105-161-3

A catalogue record for this book is available from the British Library

Animal Alphabet

Written by Joshua George

Illustrated by Zhanna Ovocheva

Look inside, who can you see?
It's time to learn your a,b,c!

From a ...

... to **Z**!

There's an animal friend for every letter of the alphabet!

a is for alligator,

b is for bear,

c is for cat,
who has stripy hair.

d is for dolphin,

e is for eel,

f is for fox,
whose tail's soft to feel.

g is for goose,

h is for horse,

i is for iguana,
(he's a lizard,
of course).

j is for jaguar,

k is for kiwi,

L is for lion, who we all want to see!

m is for monkey,

n is for nightingale,

O is for otter,
who has a long tail.

p is for penguin,

q is for queen bee,

r is for raccoons,
(they're very naughty).

S is for squirrel,

t is for turkey,

U is for urchins,
with their spines so perky.

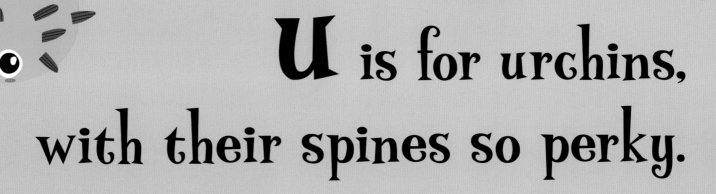

V is for vulture,

W is for whale,

X is for x-ray tetra,
with their see-through scales!

Y is for yak,
(and for Yorkshire terrier) ...

Z is for zebra -
the more, the merrier!

is for alligator

is for bear

is for cat

is for dolphin

is for eel

is for kiwi

is for lion

is for monkey

is for nightingale

is for otter

is for urchin

is for vulture

is for whale

is for x-ray tetra

is for fox

is for goose

is for horse

is for iguana

is for jaguar

is for penguin

is for queen bee

is for raccoon

is for squirrel

is for turkey

is for yak

is for zebra